Pictures in my mind

JOAN POULSON

Illustrated by David Roberts

MACDONALD YOUNG BOOKS

For friends

Text copyright © Joan Poulson 1999
Illustrations copyright © David Roberts 1999

First published in Great Britain in 1999
by Macdonald Young Books
an imprint of Wayland Publishers Ltd
61 Western Road
Hove
East Sussex
BN3 1JD

Find Macdonald Young Books on the internet at
http://www.myb.co.uk

The following poems were first published as follows:
Our Farm, January: (The Educational Company of Ireland. 1991).
Shorthand: Excuses, Excuses. (O.U.P. 1997).
some game: Excuses, Excuses. (O.U.P. 1997).
All That Space: Dark as a Midnight Dream. (Evans Bros. 1998)
Graffiti: Footprints on the Page. (Evans Bros. 1998).

Designed by Don Martin
Printed and bound by Guernsey Press

British Library Cataloguing in Publication Data available

ISBN: 0 7500 2828 9

Contents

Introduction

For me, poetry is endless satisfaction – the reading and the writing of it. I love the sounds, images and rhythms. I love the way one image or phrase can produce several different meanings. I love the fun of it!

Poetry satisfies the part of me that is intrigued by mystery and fascinated to think of the how, the why, of things: tiny things like bees, ants, snowflakes and bigger (but still tiny) things like people. The enormous things have always interested me. When I was young they scared me: how far is the end of the world, how much are the stars, where does a person begin and end, do people ever end, do people and 'things' – mountains, trees, moths, ducks – ever overlap?

Some poems come from seeing connections: I might have one experience and soon afterwards something, perhaps something totally different, happens. Suddenly I see a connection! *Imagine* is a poem which came in this way. I had been working with elderly people in a residential home. They were enthusiastic writers, rich in experience and generous humour. On my way home, I stopped at an Indian shop in the city and bought some of my favourite sweetmeats. I recalled conversations I'd had with Indian friends on short visits to their country. Suddenly the idea for *Imagine* was there.

The idea for *blue planet* came from nowhere. It was one of those gifts that writers occasionally receive. Gift poems simply arrive. They present themselves on the doorstep of your mind. You know a poem is there, you open the door and it enters slowly. A gift. You write on. When you have finished you read with surprise what you have written.

Some of my gifts have been *Song about a Drummer* and *Our Farm, January*.

As with most writers, things I believe to be true underpin what I write. I also like to laugh, finding humour in all kinds of situations. Sometimes I write about problems and difficulties young people experience at school or in the family. Reading a poem about someone else's difficulties helps us realize the problem is shared. It might be something someone in my own family has talked about but I also have vivid memories of how I felt in similar situations.

Each time I write a poem it is always as if it is happening for the first time. Initially it is an "allowing", giving space to the poem. As I write I try not to think of anything else. When I have the first draft, the work of crafting begins: playing with words and rhythms, finding stronger images and fresh metaphors – writing and re-writing until you have the poem you want, the only one that will give you satisfaction.

Joan Poulson

David Roberts was runner-up for the 1999 Mother Goose Award for his illustrations in Roy Apps' *Frankie Stein's Robot* (also published by Macdonald Young Books).

Pictures in my Mind

One of those those massive lizards
with swivel-cone eyes, on the track.
It's camouflaged, sand-brown as the rocks.

We've not had a foreign holiday before,
seen sky that's blue as hyacinths,
water like a rainbow.

At home the beck is brown as peat
but the sea's horizon is purple
then it sweeps to the shore in bands of silk:
turquoise, emerald, lapis-blue…
as if someone has speckled it
in dancing silver.

I love living up on the moor
and this time of year
the colours are like old tweed
with everywhere rough and raw.
But the sand is soft,
colour of a mermaid's hair
and when the tide is going out   .
you find tiny pink and yellow stones,
hermit crabs tucked in shell-homes,
sand-smoothed glass: jade, opal, topaz. ☛

On Monday I bought a mask and snorkel
and swam with Dad to the mouth of the
   cove.
It was an underwater festival: fish colourful
as Morris dancers, striped and spotty as
   clowns
– standing on their heads to feed
among plants that grow on rocks.

Tomorrow we fly home.
It will be wet and cold, grey,
harsh as granite on the moor.
Like a different planet.
I love it, never want to live in any other
    place
but all winter when it sleets or there's fog,
when the snow throws thick blankets
over the farm, the Shippons, the barn,
right up... over the Crag, down the valley,
I can have pictures in my mind
– be able to close my eyes
and see this cove, those fish,
the clear shimmering colours.
I'll taste ocean-tang, smell saltwater,
hear Mum and Dad's laughter...

And I'll feel more satisfied in my own place
knowing things like this exist,
knowing how rich and diverse my world is.

A Cunning Child

I'm going to build a den
down our garden, right at the end,
as far away as I can from our Roseanne.

Mum and Dad don't know
what justice means – to them,
being fair is about the colour of your hair.

If you're small and podgy-cuddly,
no one ever yells at you
whatever stupid things you do.

They put on syrupy voices,
use baby-talk, save their threats
and foul words for me...

and our Roseanne responds a treat.
She's smart and sly, tricky as a vixen
that's well educated

in the ways of the wild.
A cunning child, my little sister
but I'm the only one who's sussed her...

yet. Next week they can suffer,
find out what she's really like.
I'll be safe in my den

and Roseanne won't go down there:
I've made sure she knows it's where
the fiercely monstrous

Clints and Grykes have their lair...
and if there's one thing they love
most of all to eat

it's podgy little cuddly sweet

SISTERS.

a devil on my back

got a monster on my shoulder
got a devil on my back
dragging me this way
snatching me that

everyone watching
can't they see
the way I'm being shoved about
lost
the real me

some say
they've got the answer
will sell me some
cheap

I've got the money
that's no problem
why hesitate?

got a monster on my shoulder
got a devil on my back
telling me I'm no good
convincing me I'm trash

they say it's like flying
in endless space
say – can't get hooked
try it
you'll just feel ace!

where else
can I go?

where can I be free

from this monster
this devil
forever slamming me?

A Sister is Different

(for my sister)

Ever since I started school
my big sister's been there too.

Until this week.

Now she's going to high school
and I've got two more years to go,
here, on my own.

No one there for me...

I suppose I'm quite lucky,
I've got really good friends
and I like being popular.
But a sister is different.
I really miss her.

It's a bit like when grandad died,
only everyone thought that was all right.

When you cry because someone's died
it's what they expect.
Everyone knows you must be sad.
But not for this!
I'm sure they'll all start calling me cissy
if they find out how much I miss my sister.

A Wave like a Whale

(for Yanni)

It starts with us playing on the edge.
The sea is savage
and Dad begins swimming.
Don't go out there! Mum looks scared.

He's got medals, don't forget, Kev says.
But this is no leisure centre
– the sea here is like the inside
of a washing machine.

The tide's going out! Mum shouts.
Dad doesn't hear.
Our Shamina starts to cry.
Soft-head! Mum tries to smile.

I climb the rocks,
see Dad swimming…
further, further…
Then… he turns.

He's coming back! I'm yelling
when a wave like a whale
eats him.
I think I scream.

Suddenly
I see him
and he's swimming…
swimming…

He really tries –
arms powerful scythes,
but it's like some sea-monster
has him on a line

towing him,
quite slowly,
sideways and round the point.
Out of sight.

Dad! I'm screaming. *Dad!*
Then I'm crying, too
and I'm running, stumbling,
racing for where he disappeared.

And stop... daren't go closer.
I just stand there
and I'm shivering,
turning to look for Mum.

When
in the corner of my eye
there's a movement.
I swing round, see a head...

Dad!
scrambling into sight,
chest and arms clawed raw,
blood like becks...

but he's grinning...
and I'm in his arms.
Dad! You're alive!
It's Shamina yelling.

Yes, I am, love, Dad whispers.
Then they all fling on him –
me in the middle, squashed flat
as a jelly-fish on the beach.

Better get you to hospital!
Mum says at last.
We're all looking at the blood.
O, no, not for that! Mum says.

*It's a surgeon
your father needs.
A surgeon...
and a brain transplant!*

A Wish

He's old,
the oldest person
I've ever known.

He's small and frail,
looks as if the faintest
puff of wind
will snuff him out

a candle
still burning
when others have flickered
without us noticing
and gone.

One of the few
surviving his generation.

His light
slightly dim
but not much else
is feeble about him...

He's strong enough
to fetch in coal,
make the fire every day,
tough enough to challenge
when they tried to make him say
he'd leave his home...

He locked the door,
yelled when they came
No more messing!
No more games!
This is war
and I'm not leaving
so you'll have to smoke me out!

He made the headlines
and he's still there, in his house.
I shop for him and we play chess,
do crosswords.
He's the brains, I'm the eyes.
We won a prize once.

☞

I know someday,
maybe not too far off, he'll...
go away. And I'm afraid,
thinking about that.
It'll be so much worse
than when our Fozzle was put down
and sometimes I cry at night,
imagining that gap... new gap,
in my life.

I wish people you care about
didn't have to... go away

        people you love
    didn't die.

ALONE

Today
I was a Tiger Shark
for half an hour

slipped into

body gliding
through wa̶

just water
and me

surging, pov̶

in water

where being̶
is Tiger Sha̶

is strong.

All that Space

Great-grandad
used to tell me stories,
tales about when he was a lad,

fled city streets,
flew on his bike
down lanes between cornfields,
past Kenyon's Brick Works
to the Moss,

sitting for hours
in all that space,

played his mouth organ,
and watched...
peewits   wild violets   silhouette
of chimneys against the sky,

his shabby jersey, battered clogs,
livened by new-moon-silver buds of willow,
baby-skin softness of dog-rose petal.

In the Home, people try to interest him
in television, don't understand
when he turns his chair to the wall,
the print of Constable's Hay Wain,
curves his fingers round
his smiling mouth,
and tilts his head, listening...

sits for hours   in all that space.

Bagel

I'm beginning to look like a bagel:
round and smooth and white.

I can't cook
and since Dad left
Mum's been so stressed
she won't go out
so we don't get proper meals.
No spaghetti, no risotto (Dad's favourite).
We never have his speciality, meat balls.
He used to make them Sundays
with herby, soured-cream sauce
and corn on the cob (*my* favourite).
Mum used to laugh, say I'd turn into one.

Now it's bagels, bagels, bagels every day –
the only thing Mum will make.
I used to like them
but I'd rather be a corn cob than a bagel.
Mum would have laughed at that, once.
Now she shouts and sobs
and I don't know what to do.
Dad never writes.
I can't cook...

but this weekend... I'm going to try!
Who wants to spend the rest of their life
looking like a bagel!

Little Pig's Tuffet

Down the sugar-plum market
on a lemonade day,
the Three Little Pigs
come out to play

Best Gran

Who's the best gran?
My Gran.

Who always listens
and has always got time...

Who's the best gran?
My Gran.

Who takes me to watch rugby
(thinks her team's better than mine!)

Who's the best gran?
My Gran...

One sings a song,
   one beats her drum
      but one Little Pig
         builds a beautiful home

still reads me stories
and makes up silly rhymes,
can make me laugh
when I've had a good cry,
gives the biggest hugs,
makes the juiciest rhubarb pie.
My Gran.

So I know how lucky *I* am… don't I?

Bio-techno

They want to wipe out weeds
that they say steal sunshine,

want to make our food
in laboratories.

They want to patent seeds
and call farmers thieves.

They say bees 'usurp pollen'
say: We must kill the bees!

Kill freedom...

with a sherbet-sparkly roof,
a chocolate bar door,
a gold and amber pancake
spread upon the floor.

Blushing Blues

I got the blues
got them bad

got to sing
though it makes me sad

I got the blushing blues
red as a rag to a bull.

I wake up in the morning
fall out of my bed
climb into my blue jeans
put on my head
all the time wondering
what the day will bring
how many times
I'll have to sing...
I got the blues
got them bad

got to sing
though it makes me sad

I got the blushing blues
red as a rag to a bull.

Then that Little Pig
    finds her stripy piano-tuffet
        and plays duet chopsticks
            with little Miss Muffet.

BLUE

Blue

is when
someone paints you
inside
with tears

seals your eyes
with wax

Brilliant, Like Me!

Today I went with Mum and Dad
on the bus and the train for our baby.

It took us three hours to travel
all that way but we knew
she'd be worth the long journey.

Our baby and me are adopted
but we both have freckly skin,
and I laughed today when I saw her
– she gave me a gummy grin.

I laughed when I saw her
– she looks just like me!
She's even got a funny, pointy chin.

I'm glad Mum and Dad chose our baby.
I'm glad they both chose me.

It's going to be great
to have a little sister.

I think she's brilliant –
like me!

COMPUTER SPEAK

We went to London on the train,
saw this famous artist's pottery
in a big exhibition.

His pots are not like ours at home:
jugs, cups, plates,
things you can use.

It's more like stuff our Kate,
my kid sister, might make:
fantastic shapes,

covered in blobs or sticky-out bits,
faces painted on them, brilliant colours.
They made me laugh. I liked them.

When I read the leaflet
I thought about Gran
and how she's like this man...

not an artist, not famous
but because of how she thinks.
Especially about computers.

Use your brain! she says.
Give that machine a rest.
Computers are not so great...

Think about it, she says.
When did a computer
ever ask a good question

Calls Himself a Teacher

I can't stand that man!
Calls himself a teacher
but I don't know how he can

or how he's got the nerve
to take money
for the rubbish he serves up
every waste-of-time day.

But I'm sure
I'd despise him even more
if he wasn't such a mess.
Pathetic!
Face covered in moon-craters
and skinny, bandy legs
like a bony, old frog.

You have to laugh!

I said to my Gran:
If that's a man, give me
a loose-leaf notebook any day!

Got the Hump

Gran says
if she were a witch
she'd turn our cat
(who's grumpy,
who's always got the hump)
into a camel.

I'd like that,
no one else
in our street
has a camel-flap.

Finding my Own Way

I didn't think
of being popular,
just hoped
I'd be accepted

but wasn't really surprised
when they began
to shut me out,
call me names.

I'd half-expected it.

At times I'd get wild,
try to defend myself.
They only laughed.

At times I felt like crying
and they could tell,
seemed to enjoy it.

Last week I told my Dad.
He was glad I'd let him know,
thought if I tried
not to show I minded,
if I stuck it out

they might lose interest,
find something else
equally useless to do.

After all, it can't be much fun
tormenting someone...
if they ignore it, don't react.

Yesterday
two lads from my class asked
if I'd join a game with them.

It might be a start. Who knows.
And I think Dad's great,
but it's time to find my own way
out of this mess...
Today I'm going to tell Miss Bexley.

glad me

glad me
  with
      peacock-green ocean waves
        glisten in the sun
          like crystal
            or tears

glad me
  with
      bronze-red beech leaves
        glow in the rain
          like sunset
            or flame

glad me
  with
      down-light snowflakes
        filigree in frost
          like flowers
            or stars

glad me
with
    smoke-soft rivers
     secretive in fog
      like whispers
       or veils

glad me
with life

glad me
my world.

GRAFFITI

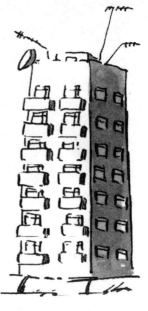

Over the tracks
back of the flats
it's growing
like a garden.

Round the streets
all concrete
no grass, no trees
nothing green

but

over the tracks
back of the flats
it's growing
like a garden.

There's every colour
you can think of
every shape
every size

words spark
like fire-works
jazzy, dazzling –
mind your eyes.

Zig-zag letters
fizzle and fall,
squiggles, splodges
surprising the wall.

Spiralling showers
luminous, bright,
fluorescent flowers
fresh overnight.

Over the tracks
back of the flats
it's growing
like a garden.

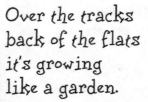

Green Witch

Today in my garden
I saw the Green Witch,
her eyes were glowing,
dark as pitch.
Her skin, her gown, her hair,
her bones – green as the ivy,
green as mossed stones.

She held out her hand,
whispered: *Come with me,*
to the shores of the dolphin,
the emerald sea.
I will show you moor, beck
and fell,
let you fly with the swallow,
take the wild geese trail.

In the deep of her eyes,
her hair's willowy strands,
in her wide curving mouth,
her strong open hands,
I saw and I heard,
I felt and could smell,
things I'd forgotten, things I knew well.

Today in my garden
my heart opened wide…
but life here is safe,
some things must stay outside.
So I slammed shut the door,
will not risk again… but can never
shut out the pain, the pain, the pain

in those deep-glowing eyes.

Having to Change

I don't want any more change,
there's already been too much.
After Dad left we moved house twice
– everything different
but I kept my same school,
kept all my mates.

After Grandma died
Mum got a child-minder.
Everything different
but I kept my same school,
kept all my mates.

Mum married again
and Bill's all right.
We moved to his place.
It's big, got an ace garden
down by the beck.
Everything different
but I kept my same school,
kept all my mates.

Now it's summer holidays
and we're going to Spain.
Bill says the beaches are great
and he'll let me stay up late
with him and Mum, some nights.
He says it's always sunny
and I'll love the food
but no one's talking about when we get
   home,
when I start the new school
where none of my mates are going,
where everyone except my year
will be older, bigger, smarter
and I'm scared of what they'll do.

I daren't tell Mum
she says I'm lucky, going there,
and Bill's all right
but he'd never understand in a
   million years
if I said I was scared.

Yesterday I called for Specs.
His mum said he'd gone down the Rec',
with Buzzer and Mack.
Mack's my best mate, got a new bike
for when he starts his new school
– the one they're all going to, except me.

I didn't go looking down the Rec'.
Might as well get used to being on my own,
I thought. So I went home.

And I talked to Dad on the phone,
knew he'd understand.
Keep your head down and do your best,
    he said.
You'll be all right.
He reminded me how scared I was
when I first started school –
Everything was new
but look at all the friends you made.
You'll be all right!

I felt a bit better when I went to bed.
Today I'm not sure.

Now Mack's here...
at the back door with Buzzer and Specs.
They want me to go down the Rec'
want a game of footie...

I was always best player, always on the
school team...
maybe I will be again.

IMAGINE

My friend Shahiz has a granny in India.
Well, her dad's granny really.
She lives in a village in the forest
where there's no TV no cars or
   make-up kits
and no one goes to school!
I really like that bit
but stared at Shahiz when she told me.
'Can't imagine it!' I said.

'In the village no one has to live alone,
or in a Home,' she said.
'At night people tell each other stories
about the village long ago,
or from the Mahabharata
– they all remember different parts
and sit in darkness, under stars,
sharing in the telling.
Far away a panther coughs, monkeys
   screech,
but everyone listens to Krishna's
   adventures.'
'Can't imagine it,' I said...

It's different, innit, when it's not on telly,
when your best mate tells you
and that's someone like Shahiz –
dead cool, purple highlights in her hair...

I stared at her,
tried to imagine living in that village,
tried to see myself there... but couldn't.

It's Worrying Me

I've got this problem, see.
It's my girlfriend.

Well, she's not the problem
but in a way
she is
because
she keeps asking me
to kiss her.

Sometimes
I grin or wink
or I pucker my lips.

Sometimes I smile…
mysteriously,
romantically.

But
I don't think
she's convinced.

And it's worrying me.

Even if we finish

there'll be someone else soon
and they're sure to want to kiss.
Girls do.

I think I'd be all right

if I knew
how
to get started

if I knew
what it is you do.

Jacob and the Angel

I went to an art gallery with Dad
saw a dead lobster
flame red
lying on a telephone

some strange paintings
one of hands holding a knife and fork
eating their own insides

a man riding a rhinoceros
across the sky

then I saw these two massive men
a sculpture

one of them had wings

his hands were holding Jacob
as if he cared
that Jacob was very sad and scared

later we sat on the grass outside
had our picnic

and everywhere

that man's hands.

Let me in

Last month we moved
and came to live
in this little house
in this little street
in this little dark little town

and I have to go to this rotten school
– school for zombied chimpanzees,
where I get called stuck-up
               and worse.

Names like…
well, half what they say
sounds like gibberish,
ape-talk.
How can I be expected to answer,
when I don't understand what they mean.
So I stand there. And wait.
Hoping they'll maybe put it in English.
Hoping they'll maybe explain.

But then I'm called thicko
              or worse.

If I give up, walk away, I'm a snob-pig.
Whatever I do I can't win.

I watch them
watching me
and I'm thinking
they don't ever mean
to be friends, let me in.

And I'm thinking
they're thinking
how useful I've been
when they've had a bad morning with
    Binns.

And they're always bad mornings with him.

Alive

pu-dthum   pu-dthum   pu-dthum

life rhythm
inside

pu-dthum   pu-dthum   pu-dthum

keeping me
alive

heart beat drum   going on
and on

pulse life rhythm
how
I survive

outside me
the sun
keeping me alive

outside   life rhythm
how
I survive

my heart   *the sun**
pu-dthum   *pu-dthum*

heart   *outside*
going on and on

pu-dthum   *pu-dthum*
    heart   *beat*   *sun.*

* *The Sun My Heart* Thich Nhat Hahn
  (Pub: Parallax Press, USA)

Music-maker

Keep going
wi' your head down,
Great-grandad always says.
I like listening to his stories
about the old days.

Keep goin'
wi' your head down,
it'll turn out awreet!

Every time he got new clogs,
made his ankles bleed.
Saturdays he ran errands,
ha'penny a time – some he flattened
to penny size on the tram-line,
then down to the railway station
and the chocolate slot-machine.
Penny bars of chocolate
made his blue eyes gleam.

*Keep goin'
wi' your head down,
it'll turn out awreet!*

Dragging his feet.
Ankles bleed.
Saving-up ha'pennies week by week.

His mam took in washing,
made jam and nettle beer,
sold it from the back-yard gate
to buy his winter gear:
a jersey and a pair of clogs
so he could go to school.
*Keep goin'
wi' your head down!*
Great-grandad's only rule.

Dragging his feet week by week.
Saving-up ha'pennies...
It'll turn out awreet.

Bought a mouth organ,
taught himself to play.
Lapis-eyes dancing,
making music every day.

Now everyone's saying:
He turned out awreet!
Giving him a party down our street.

People here to see him,
they've come from miles around.
Headline in the "Daily News":
Best Music-maker in Town!

My Poem

*I wrote a poem
in school
yesterday.*

Shortest poem I ever made:
Last week
my grandad
died.

*Yesterday
in school
I wrote a poem.*

*One day last week:
yesterday
my grandad
was still alive.*

My Wings

If I could fly
I'd have wings
golden as a tiger's eye

soft and strong
as water
rolling
silk-like
over rock
hollowing stone
turning bone to silt.

My wings
silent as sky
would hold me
motion   less

space
between breaths

enormous
vulnerable
as a heart's feathering.

Mystery

Where did it come from,
the idea of Human Beings:
people... walking, talking, thinking,
who can run, write, reason.

People made of carbon and potassium,
more than 80% water
and with waterproof skin,
a jointed bone structure,
muscles, blood and a heart that is there,
beating, right from the start.

When did my heart begin?

And which came first...
the blood... or the beat?

It's a mystery, all of it,
a mystery to me...

I wish I could have an idea
half as good!

New Man

Bruno's lived with me
since I was six.
It might seem daft,
calling a rabbit Bruno
but I had a guinea-pig
called Frank at the time.

Frank died when I was nine.
Old age, they told me.

Now Bruno's five.
I can't stand
the thought of him dying.
But I'd never let him suffer
and I'd know right away if he did.
He'd let me know.

Now this new man
in Mum's life
says Bruno's lived to a good age
and should be put down,
says he must be in pain.

I say
that's for Bruno to show
and me
to find out.

Not for totem-pole
to give me ear-ache about.

I know who I think
should be put down.
Poor Mum must be out of her mind!
What a guy – all
Next clothes, Armani cologne,
501's at week-end. Brain dead.

Our Farm, January

It was cold enough to freeze a snowman's
   legs off,
colder than I'd ever known before
and one morning when I got up it had
   happened,
summat as I'd waited twelve month for

– the pewtered sky had been relieved its
   burden,
the frozen grip let go its hold at last
and our farmyard, down the daleside,
all the valley out to Thirsk
was eiderdowned and safe-tucked-in,
soft and white and hushed.

I knew I'd best keep quiet about my
feelings,
it i'n't easy looking after stock i' this
and it's hard enough i' summer to mak
   a go up here,
i' winter it can crack your heart, reduce
   a man to tears...

but I love to see it look like this
our dale – and out beyond,
untouched and pure and all
   snugged-down,
feathered o'er i' snow.

real as earth

what colour the earth
that nourished the wheat
on my plate
as bread
this morning

what language
did the people speak
sowing the wheat
on my plate
as bread
this morning

how many raindrops
on each seed
before it sprouted –
small plant of wheat
on my plate
as bread
this morning

how strong the sun
and how many days
to ripen grain
on the head of wheat
on my plate
as bread
this morning

who ground the grain
made the flour
how many hours
and where the mill
who filled the sacks
and baked the bread
good and real
as earth
on my plate
this morning.

Rainbow Mad

I don't mind
when my ears go red,
when everyone stares
at something I've said.

I don't care
when my fingers turn blue,
when I've missed the bus
and I'm freezing through.

I'm not bothered
when my face looks green,
when I've read horror stories
and think I've seen

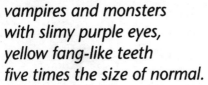

vampires and monsters
with slimy purple eyes,
yellow fang-like teeth
five times the size of normal.

But I hate it, can't take it,
turn every colour there's ever been,
when I play for our team –
aim at goal… and miss.

Rub-a-dub

Rub-a-dub-dub
    three pigs take a scrub
        in an oak tree galleon
           green bath-tub.

Riddle for the 21st Century

I used to think food
was seeds, rain, sun…

was farmers, earth, grain,
was about sowing
and growing…

Where have I been!
They're turning food
into a gene-machine.

Shorthand

Our English teacher's
punctuated.

Our Music teacher's
crotchet.

Our Science teacher's
fractal.

But our Humanities teacher's
tropic.

One plays the fiddle,
    another plays the drum.
    One makes porridge
        with a saffron baked plum.

Rugby Club

(for Sarah)

Our playing-field
is back of school,
under the moor.

Mondays
we have Rugby Club,
my favourite.
I can't wait
for Mondays –
the day
I never laik-off school.

Rugby Club – it's great!

We have running,
we have passing,
we have to skid, score tries.
But we don't have kicking
with under-nines!

Teacher blows her whistle.
We're all in pairs –
race down the field,
running like hares.

One has the ball,
the other has to tackle –
face pushed in the grass,
feel your teeth rattle.

They whistle Quite Contrary,
Morris-dance around the tree
and hey, diddle-diddle,
Big Bad Wolf eats all three.

It's what we do
at Rugby Club
back of school
under the moor:
running
passing
skidding
scoring tries.

But we don't have kicking
with under-nines!

Sun Energy

She told us today
      that earth
        exists
          on sun-energy

            uses
             one billionth

             only
             one billionth

             of the energy
             of the sun
             to exist.

        Earth:
        one sun-billionth

        ...UNBELIEVABLE!

Tell Sam

(for Jane)

When I get told off at school,
which happens all the time
because our teacher's
the worst there is,
I try not to mind. I know
when I get home
I can always tell Sam.

When Mum gets on at me,
which happens all the time
because our standards
are miles apart,
I try not to mind. I know
when I'm alone
I can always tell Sam.

When our kid wrecks a game,
which happens all the time
because he's spoiled,
a complete pain,
I try not to mind. I know
when things have quietened down
I can always tell
Top-of-the-League-Dog Sam.

some game

they played the whispering game
told the others
they must make fun of her name
drew pictures of her
passed them round the class
said she smelled
held their noses
when she walked past

and it was just
something they did
just a bit of fun

not their fault
she took it like that

not their fault

Word-tree

Half a pound of alphabet-buds
half a pound of word-leaves
taste the music
smell the sounds
dance around the poetree

Secret-name Days

I keep a diary of her days, different days.
Most of them are different.

Some she calls her Running Days.
Those are my favourite.

Mum can't really run.

Running Days are ones
where she can leave her chair at home,

days she can walk,
go in the garden on her own.

Some we call her Sitting Days.
Jet-propelled Days! Dad says:

when Mum needs her chair
but isn't in too much pain

– we go down the estuary in the car
and have a race. I always win.

Days we never name
are when the pain's so bad

Mum stays in bed.
My secret name for them:

name that can't be said,
one I scream in my pillow

when Mum's managed
to get to sleep...

   ...dreaming...

...nightmares... screaming...

...slice... slash... hate...

hate them...

BROKEN GLASS DAYS

Skrike-place

(in memory of Wilfred Sykes)

It's red like *Quinquereme of Ninevah*.
Two men shove it on a little trolley
to the water. I follow it in.

The sea's cold, sand soft and ripply
between my toes. I can't swim.

On the sands the others build castles,
dads doze in deckchairs under hankies,
mams expand like sea anemones.

I breathe in shell-grey space.

Waves slap my waist, my chest,
shock my pale skin.

They switch the engine on,
boat headed for some place
in poems Mr Sykes read.

Seagulls skrike.
Misty voices.

One more step

and I am swallowed,
gulp seawater like air.

The others build castles.
I splash back, breathless
but become my own heroine.

When I try to tell them they smile,
turn back to chat and cups of tea.

I feel that skriking in my belly,
in my skrike-place,

turn away
make my little sister laugh.

Snail-storm

Our back-yard's a jungle:
plants that swarm and tumble,
up the fence, across the flags
and the only patch of earth,
tangling down from shelves
Mum fixed to the wall and made
from planks on piles of bricks.

She's planted shrubs in tubs,
in buckets and old tyres she found
on the Tip, scattered seed
along the bottom of the wall
down our Back so in summer
it's a mass of marigolds and daisies,
cornflowers and hazy love-in-a-mist.

A frog lives in a clump of thyme,
oregano and moss. We've got worms
like the Loch Ness Monster.
For Mum's birthday Dad bought her
a huge hosta. *A jewel!* she said.
Look at the leaves –
striped emerald and amethyst.

Word is out of course, that she's green
as Celtic's strip, thinks diversity
is what life's about – so every slug
and snail for miles comes to our yard.
That's all right, there's plenty for them all,
Mum says. *They're as entitled*
to what's here as we are.

This week we've been on holiday,
stayed in Gran's little caravan in the Lakes.
You should have seen our yard
when we got back – as if there'd been
hailstorms of stripy humbugs every day!
And not just our usual lot, some of them
are massive! Down from the city, I'd say. ☞

89

I felt sorry for Mum – her hosta
tattered ribbons. She looked sad…
then stood up, shrugged,
said she'd give the snails a holiday,
take them down the Causeway.
I don't know where she gets the patience
– maybe she buys seed and grows it!

I know if it was left to me it would be
Hasta la vista, senores snails!

Snakes and Ladders

Today's my last day at Bedford Street.
Our School.
In some ways I'm glad:
not to have to see Mad Murray any more
or put up with Mrs Paine's feeble jokes
and especially not having Mr Embleton
    for sports,
showing what a wimp he really is.
But it's the only school I've been to,
all my friends come here,
everyone in our street,
everyone I've known since I was little.

They say they flush your head down
    the loo
– and there's all the tests, too...
Tests scare me, even in Our School
but the ones at the comprehensive
are different. Difficult. Important.

You feel like you're in a game,
picked up and moved without having any
    say.
A pawn. A castle slid across the board.
A counter landing on a snake and slipping
    down…
From the top to the bottom
in one shake of the dice.

And all the time you pretend:
Yeah, it's fantastic!
Yeah, I'm really looking forward…
Yeah, can't wait.

All the time wishing you could emigrate,
there'd be an earthquake,
someone would discover the Big Mistake
– you and your mates should all be going
to the same school, can stay there till
    you finish.

But then there's all that grown-up stuff
– starting work, unemployment,
paying the rent, forms to fill in.

This game   it's one you can't win.

...fantastic... looking forward... can't wait...

So Long Ago

My mum has a granny
who was in the war.
She's very old and wobbly,
can't walk far

but she tells fantastic stories,
makes us cry, makes us laugh.
They're vivid, sometimes scary,
about soldiers she nursed.

She talks about the friends she made,
like one my mum calls Auntie Bea
who lives in a Home,
can hardly see;

another mum calls
Uncle Joe – he still plays
the cornet, sings:
Hear this man blow!

My mum has a granny
who was in the war,
talks about the friends she made,
all very old, all very brave,

they did what they did
though they were all afraid
but all say: *Given my chance again,
I'd never let them send me off to war!*

Song About a Drummer

O my mammy sang a song
about a drummer down the cellar
but this green-eyed drummer
was no ordinary feller
he'd a purple chimney hat,
a crazy, steeleye band,
wore yellow high-heeled boots,
carried magic in his hand...

magic in the drumsticks
dub-a-dub, beat,
frizzle-up your furlylocks
rap-tap through your feet...

and the purple chimney hat
rang with the voice of the drum
and the crazy, steeleye band
sang calypsos to the sun.
In his yellow high-heeled boots
the drummer leaped from the cellar
and my mammy led him dancing
where the waves crash and bellow

there they rap-tap whirled
till the moon grew pale
saw them twirl into the sun-rise
on a gentian-backed whale
and my silver-haired mammy
kept the secret of the cellar
never telling
where the drummer could be found...

magic in the drumsticks
dub-a-dub, beat,
frizzle-up your furlylocks
rap-tap through your feet.

Spirals

When my brother was a baby
he had tiny blobby toes,
not much hair,
soft silky skin
all over, just enough.

Now my brother's five,
his bones have grown bigger
so he's a lot taller,
skin much rougher
but still covering him all over,
just enough.

I'm twelve
and I keep wondering
how my bones will know
when to stop growing,
if I'll ever
run out of skin.

I look at my finger-tips,
each with a spiral, each spiral different
and wonder...

about my skin, about those spirals
made of tiny cells.

Mrs Barker says
scientists believe that every cell
in existence
contains *all* of life…

It's amazing. A massive idea.
But *all* of life   in *every* cell?

Makes me think I must be ENORMOUS.

Storybook Life

I wish I had a storybook life

with a sister
who is cute,
a funny little brother
and a mum
and a dad
and a dog
who's just mine.

I'd have a gran and grandad
with a farm,
an uncle in Texas
who'd take us to his ranch
to stay forever
then
I'd never
have to see our Liz again.

I suppose Mum's all right really
and at least our Blackie races
like a jet
across the Rec'
when I whistle.

I suppose my ugly sister Liz
is not that bad...
but I'd quite like a kid brother.

And I really miss my dad.

Street Cred

(for NC)

I didn't hear a thing,
was down the cellar
with the rest of my mates,
sound level raised as far as it would go.

'Welcome! Welcome!' Mum said
when she saw Fizz and Slatts at the door.
'Welcome to Fred Fazackerley's Bicycle
    Shed!'
They didn't know but that afternoon
their two bikes were the final straw.

'Come in, don't just stand there
– I enjoy having this icy wind roaring
round the house,
but all the rubbish blowing in
might clog up the vacuum cleaner.
If I ever get time to use it, that is!'

'Can we bring them in... our bikes?'
mumbled Fizz.
'They might get pinched, see.'
'Oh, yes, I do agree!' Mum cried.
'Bring them inside and... well...
just toss them on this pile.
It's like the Wall of Death anyway,
you may as well make it thoroughly
    monumental!'

Fizz and Slatts dumped their bikes
and raced downstairs
but it was hours before they told me
and by then it was too late
– Mum had gone completely mental.
She'd rung up all her mates
– racing round the estate they were
doing wheelies on our bikes...
everyone had come outside,
clapping and cheering them on.
And she was wearing my baseball cap!

It's all right for her, she's only
a social worker.
Me, I'll never live it down.

This might not sound serious

but I don't like my laugh

sounds like a hyena
that's got a bad cough

and sometimes I hiccough
then that makes me giggle

so I'm choking and whooping
with spits in the middle.

I've tried every cure
from thinking of death

to holding my nose
to stop-off my breath

but nothing will change it,
nothing will work

whatever I've tried
seems to make my laugh worse

– my barking gets louder,
the hiccoughing giggles

rise to rhino-staccato,
drop to jelly-fish-dribbles.

When the circus is over,
I'm weak and wet through.

It's hard work is laughing
– when your laugh's like a zoo.

TOSH

Before they moved next door
I thought it would be great –
having a mate so close.

We heard they had three children,
one same age as me.
I wanted to meet her.

They pushed her in a wheel-chair.
Frankly, I just stared, didn't want
to know, then – or care.

I'd hear her, yelling, see her
trundling up and down the path,
raging or rocking with laughter.

And it was that laugh
as well as the kind of thing
she said…

Tosh might not walk
and it was difficult at first
to understand, the way she talks

but I realized I was the one
who lived small and scared,
not her.

I was the one
who lived a limited life,
not her.

Yeah, she has a rotten temper
– so have I. Sometimes she says things
that hurt – so do I.

But Tosh gets involved, takes risks, tries.
She's not afraid to make mistakes...
She laughs, cries,

lets us all know what's real.
And that wild girl Tosh is real!
Really alive.

Touch the Sun

I can't float up to the sky,
feel moistness of cloud
on my fingers, my face.

I couldn't touch the sun,
stroke its glowing curves
without burning...

but when I touch a daisy,
bougainvillea, linnaea borealis,*
I touch moisture and heat,
touch rain and sun
that made each flower become...

touch them
in every petal, every stamen.

* flower found in Norway and Sweden, named after the
Swedish botanist Carl von Linne. Linnaea is often
found growing with the plant pyrola: the two small
plants are sometimes referred to as 'the pride of
Scandinavian flowers'.

Uncle Bill

Uncle Bill is a jogger,
among other things.

But it shouldn't be allowed,
and if they made a movie of him
then it wouldn't be allowed
on the screen.

Or not without a Double X certificate.

To put a body like my uncle's
into shorts... well, it's obscene
– he's a melting Easter-egg,
and you've never seen *anything*
to equal his great legs:
corrugated carrots going mouldy!
It's a sight to strike a chill
evil as the worst of horror films.

But it's fantastic!
What a thrill!
You should hear me cheer
my carrot-legged, Easter-eggy,
brilliant Uncle Bill
when he runs in a marathon
and wins!

Who Are They?

Who are they
who are carving-up
my world?

Who are they
polluting
our seas,
cutting down trees,
stealing
my history
      my future?

thieves...

Future is coming future is now what are they saying
what will they do?

thieves

Who are they
who cannot feel
when seals bleed,   *thieves*
when fish are diseased,
when thrush and skylark song
is extinguished?

killers

Who are these
twenty-first century ogres

dragons…

Future is coming
future is now…   *dragons*

thieves

Where are you   Buddica?   Arthur?   George?

Where are you?

                    are you…
YOU!

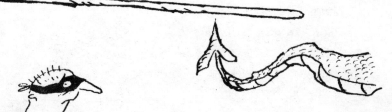

111

What to do

I love him
but he's dumped me
and I don't know
what to do.

Yesterday
I bunked off school.
I know if I keep on
I'll be a fool

but I'm not sure
what else to do...

My mates are ace.
It's the others are the trouble
– talking behind my back
and all that.

Maybe if I pretend I don't care
when they giggle and stare...

if I look strong,
try to look as if I'm happy,
ask my mates to come round
for burgers, a video,

*it might give the others
something new to talk about*

*and I could
ask that lad
from Mr Grainey's class
to come round too...*

Oh no, not angels again!

I thought Mum was going round the bend,
not just because she says angels are real
but she says she can 'feel
their presence' when she's low or sad,
says they help her about Dad:
his long illness, death.
'When I talk to them,' she says, 'their breath
is soft and fragrant on my cheek.
It's as if they speak,
silently, their voices calm and strong.'
I love Mum but sometimes she gets it totally wrong.

Yesterday Suzy, my big sister
locked herself upstairs, missed her bus,
said she wasn't going in to school any more.
So there's Mum sitting by Suzy's door,
talking for over an hour. I heard
her go on about them... that word!
She told Suzy we've all got
a guardian angel! But I said that's not
what our Su needs. 'A steam-roller
or machete would be more effective.' I told her.
'Get your mates at the Youth Club in,
give those bullies a hiding
they won't forget.'
It's horrible, I hate our Suzy being so upset!

Mum ran us in because we were late,
dropped us at the gate.
I asked Su if she'd be all right.
'I think so. And Mum's coming to see Old Spice
before she goes to work.
I'll go too but I'm going to Mrs Bell first.
I know I can trust her.
I should have gone before but I was scared.
It's crazy how fear can stop you thinking
straight.
Now – I'm not running any more. I'll fight!
But I need help, so I'll get it: Mum, Old Spice,
Mrs Bell.'
She grinned. 'And there's always my guardian
angel!'
She swung away, marched off towards the
door.

On her back, round her shoulders,
as if someone had put an arm, or something,
there...
lots of little feathers.

They Muddle Me Up

always told me
she was my mum

she's always been my mum

but last week
my big sister Jenny had a baby

and they say it's my brother

they muddle me up

Jenny told me she's my mother
says I've to call my real mum 'Gran'

and my real mum cries

they muddle me up
told me a pack of lies

I love my mum
can't stand it when she gets upset
and I've decided...
I'm going to say
who my real mum is

our Jenny can say what she likes

no more lies!
I won't let them muddle me up any more

I've decided...
me and my real mum together
are strong

and I'm not going to give her up.

the blue planet —
twelve ways of looking at Earth

(for Charlotte)

space

unmannedsatellites

e.l...e.c..t.r.o..n.i..c.i..m.a.g...e.s...

.. ...c..o..n...v.e...r.t.e.d..

digitalimages

digitalimages

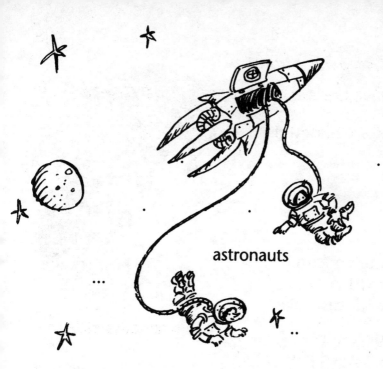

astronauts

...

i..n...f.o.r....m.a.t.i..o.n ..
..
...
...   .   o..f. e..a..r..t..h.

c.o...m.p.u...t.e..r.co...n.v.e...r....t.e.d..   .. ...

digitalimagedigitalimagedigitalimageofearth

119

i
indigo icing
swirled
on a vast cake

decoration
– carved jade
shimmers

(Moonlit photograph of Earth's horizon from
Discovery, 1994.)

ii
half-circles
big sister small sister

gold and
blue-marbled-white

(Moon and Earth from *Galileo*, December 1992.)

iii
prehistoric lizard grimaces
through the cracked opal shell
of an egg

(The Great Lakes, Mexico and parts of Central America
from *Apollo*, 16 April 1972.)

iv
slow black drag
ink splashes flung
into flame

pale peacock blue
breathed
into an ivory bracelet

(Sunset from *Endeavour*, Sept/Oct 1994.)

v
honesty petal
and pool of light
on a lilac silk coverlet

(Earth from *Discovery*, March 1989)

vi
fine salt crystal
in tiny heaps

and scattered

over a cinnabar dome
rimmed in amethyst

(Sahara Desert from *Endeavour*,
Sept/Oct 1994.)

vii

child's balloon
new-born sparrow blue
cauled white

still afloat
in the photographer's darkroom

(Earth from *Apollo 12*, November 1969.)

viii

pearly frosting
on a giant's birthday cake
tilted
for admiration

quartz-bright flash
a photographer
at work

(Tropical storm Sam off the west coast of
Australia seen from space, January 1990.)

ix

on a frozen lapis lake
           crushed ice
and scoops of melting sorbet

(Thunderstorms over the Pacific, from
Discovery, September 1994.)

x

streaked trail
fluorescent turquoise

burning-out to silver eyes
in dark purple velvet

(The southern lights seen from space, March 1994.)

xi

free-range egg yolk
on a polished slab of jet

flame enamel lid
draped in petrol-blue silk

(Layers of smoke, dust and aerosols above
a South African sunset, October 1992.)

xii

smoke-grey gauze rippled
across a slice of wet sapphire

pearl crumbs sprinkled
and painted

(Kliuchevskoi volcano, Russia,
from *Endeavour*, Sept/Oct, 1994)